Fireman Sam

and the Roof-top Rescue

Photographs by John Walker

"Hello! This is going to be an exciting day," said Trevor Evans. "I've been asked to film a rescue for the television, so I'm trying out the Fire Brigade's new video camera."

"I'm in the park and I've asked Sarah and James to help me practise using this camera," said Trevor. "Then I'll need to film a real rescue!"

Meanwhile, Dilys Price was sitting in Bella's Café and thinking that it wasn't a very exciting day. "I think I'll go home and tidy my attic," she announced to Bella.

Once home, she lit a candle and went up to the attic.
"What a muddle!" Dilys cried, looking round. "I wonder if
there is anything valuable up here?"

Dilys put her candle down on a table and peered inside a trunk. "H'mph! An old mallet," she said, carelessly throwing it over her shoulder. "And a horrid plastic doll."

Dilys didn't notice that the mallet she had thrown away had knocked her candle on to the floor. Nor did she realise that some old newspapers had caught fire.

Flames quickly spread around the attic and smoke began to billow out of the roof. Luckily the twins spotted the smoke from the street: "It's coming from Dilys' roof."

"We'd better call the Fire Brigade." Down at the station, Station Officer Steele, Fireman Sam, Elvis and Trevor all jumped to attention as the alarm began to ring.

Station Officer Steele took the urgent message: "Fire at Dilys Price's Store! Come quickly!" The firemen grabbed their equipment and dashed to Jupiter, their fire engine.

They all climbed into the cab, turned on the loud siren and set off. They knew that they must hurry for every minute counts when there is a fire.

"Do you think anyone is inside the building?" shouted
Elvis, as they roared along. "I hope not," replied Trevor.
"Poor Dilys," said Sam, "I wonder how the fire started?"

Dilys was trapped in a corner of the attic. She couldn't reach the stairs. "Is there anything in the old trunk that would help me escape?" she wondered.

Dilys grabbed a small, bronze statue from the trunk and climbed onto a chair. She lifted the statue up and smashed the lock on the skylight. "Oh, will anybody rescue me?"

Very carefully, Dilys climbed out on to the roof. She looked down the street and saw the fire engine coming. "Help! Help! I'm up here! Save me!" she cried.

The firemen jumped out. "We'll get you down in two ticks," shouted Sam as he climbed up the ladder. Then Elvis and Station Officer Steele began to put out the fire from below.

Dilys wasn't afraid of the fire anymore but she was frightened of falling and she didn't want to drop her newly found bronze statue.

"Slide down the roof," shouted Sam. Dilys sat down. She shut her eyes and let go of the chimney. "I'll catch you," promised Sam.

"Ooh! Help!" she cried, on her way down. "Don't worry," called Sam. True to his word, he stretched out his arms and caught Dilys. She was safe, but she'd lost her statue.

"Help! I've dropped my statue!" wailed Dilys. Station Officer Steele caught it. "It looks just like an Oscar," he said. "I reckon Dilys deserves one after all that screaming!"

What was Trevor doing? He wasn't rescuing Dilys like Sam or putting out the fire like Elvis and Officer Steele. He was filming the roof-top rescue with the new video camera.

"Thank you! And I'll never be so careless with candles again," Dilys promised. Later that night she sat down with Trevor and her son Norman to watch the television.

The first thing they heard on the news was, "Today in Pontypandy a dramatic roof-top rescue took place..." and there was Trevor's film, on the television!

"Look, mam, it's you!" said Norman. "Oh, dear!" said Dilys crossly. "Whatever will the neighbours say?" But secretly she was awfully pleased to be on television!